Shiny bugs

Wings cut from cupcake cases

This body is an old fuse.

Screw

This bug's body is an old plastic tube.

Cardboard tube body

Old badge for a head

See page 32 to find out how to make legs from stripped wire.

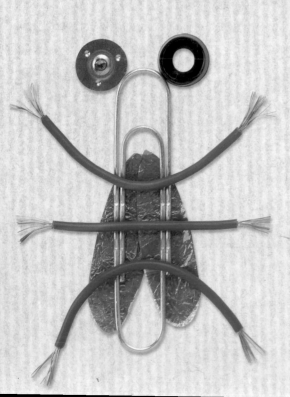

Curtain hook

Safety pin

Robot collage

You will need: scraps of wrapping paper, shiny paper, corrugated cardboard, and wrappers or foil.

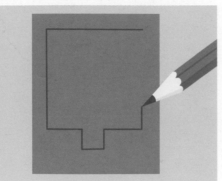

1. Draw a robot's head and neck on shiny cardboard or paper. Then, cut out the shape and glue it near the top of a piece of plain paper.

2. Cut two shapes from cardboard and glue them on either side of the head. Then, cut a nose from a wrapper and glue it onto the head.

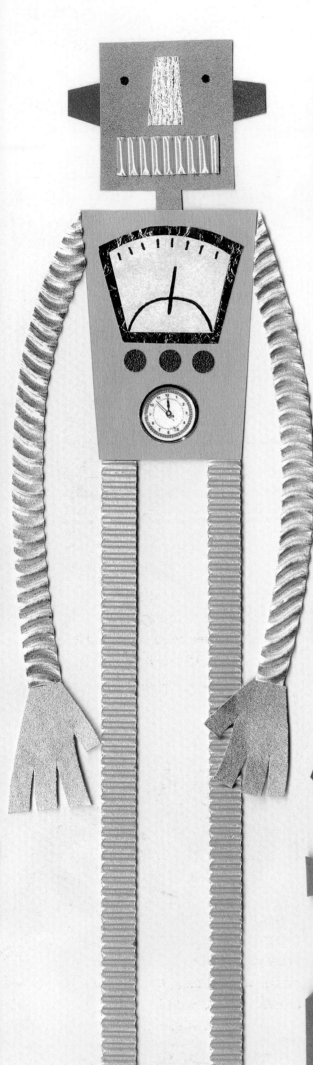

You could glue on a clock cut out from an old magazine.

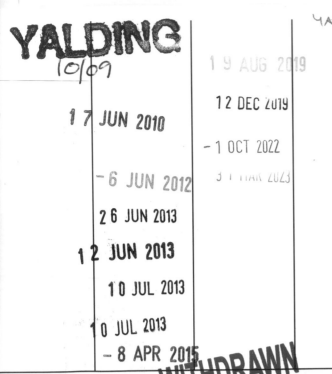

...ycling ...ngs ...make ...d do

... and Leonie Pratt

...ated by Josephine Thompson

... illustrations by Vicky Arrowsmith,
...r, Lisa Verrall, Erica Harrison and Katie Lovell
...ustrated by Jo Moore
...phs by Howard Allman

Contents

Bits and pieces

You can use almost anything you find around the house to make the things in this book. Look in your recycling bin for old boxes, cartons or wrappers.

Here are lots of things you could use. It doesn't matter if you don't have exactly the same things - try to find something similar.

Look in a toolbox for old nuts, bolts, screws, nails, washers, springs, wire...

You might find old buttons, beads, scraps of fabric, ribbons, yarn, cord or string in a sewing box...

Cardboard food boxes, cardboard tubes, shiny packaging, wrappers, plastic bags, egg cartons, bottle tops, straws...

Paper clips, rubber bands, safety pins...

Make a bug

The bug below is made from different objects stuck onto a piece of paper. Look on the next page for more ideas for bugs to make.

Magazines, comics, newspapers, old wrapping paper, tissue paper...

Part of a plastic ring from a milk carton

Scrunched up wrappers or foil

Washer

Piece of yarn or string

Large paper clip body

Nut

Wings made from chocolate wrappers

The body should overlap the neck.

3. Cut out a mouth from corrugated cardboard and glue it on. Then, cut a body from a different piece of cardboard and glue it below the head.

4. Cut two long arms from corrugated cardboard and glue them on. Then, cut two long, thin legs and glue them below the body.

You can use anything you find to make the robots. Try to use a mixture of shiny and non-shiny cardboard or wrappers.

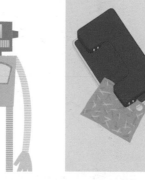

5. Cut two hands from shiny cardboard and glue them at the ends of each arm. Then, cut out a shape for a dial from cardboard.

6. Glue the dial onto a shiny wrapper and cut around it, leaving a border. Glue it onto the body. Then, punch two holes in a wrapper using a hole puncher.

You could make a picture like this one with lots of robots.

7. Open the puncher and glue the two circles above the head. Draw a black line from each circle to the head. Then, draw eyes and markings on the dial.

Tube people

You will need: cardboard tubes, magazines and newspapers, and thin cardboard or thick paper.

If your tube is very long, find out how to cut it on page 32.

Draw glasses and eyes using a black pen.

1. Paint one end of a tube for a head and leave it to dry. Then, cut strips of paper and glue them around the tube for clothes, like this.

2. Cut triangles of paper for a shirt and a bow tie. Glue them below the head. Then, cut two curved arms and fold over the ends to make tabs.

3. Spread glue on the tabs and press them onto the tube. Cut out features and glue them onto the head. Then, cut out newspaper hair and glue it on.

You could make a hat by gluing a bottle cap onto a circle of cardboard.

This girl's hair is made from yarn glued on top of the tube.

For a frilly skirt, make lots of cuts into the paper strips before gluing them on.

A dog with a box for a body and a bottle-top head

The figure above was made from a solid toothpaste tube.

Newspaper chain

You will need: newspaper.

Cut out spots, stripes and bows from scraps of paper and glue them onto the monsters.

Fold the strip in half three times.

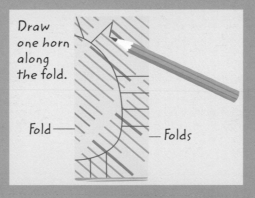

Draw one horn along the fold.

Fold — — Folds

Don't cut along the folds marked in red.

1. Cut a wide strip from a newspaper page. Fold the strip in half, short ends together, and fold it in half again. Then, fold the strip in half once more.

2. Draw a monster's body along the fold. Then, draw two arms so that they touch the edges of the paper. Add a leg, and horns on top of the head.

3. Holding the layers together, cut out the shape. Don't cut the folds by the hands. Then, unfold the paper. Use a pen to decorate the monsters.

Draw this shape on folded paper to make a cat chain.

Paper gift bags

You will need: patterned wrapping paper, magazines or comics.

Fold it so that you can see the patterned side.

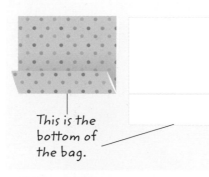

This is the bottom of the bag.

1. Cut a long rectangle from a piece of old patterned wrapping paper. Then, fold the rectangle in half so that the short ends meet.

2. Fold up the folded end of the paper to make a flap. Unfold the paper. Then, fold it again so that you can see the non-patterned side, like this.

3. With the bottom of the bag facing you, fold the top layer of paper down along the crease made in step 2. This will be one side of the bag.

For a newspaper bag, brush the paper with white glue and leave it to dry before making the bag. This will make the paper stronger.

You could use the thick paper from a magazine cover.

4. Turn over the bag, keeping the paper folded. Then, fold down the other layer of paper along the crease, to make another side.

5. Brush a line of white glue along the sides of the bag, and along the edges of the flap. Then, press the sides together until they stick.

6. For a handle, cut thick paper from a magazine into two thin strips. Fold down one end of a strip. Then, fold down the other end in the same way.

To make a big bag, cut out a bigger rectangle in step 1.

7. Fold the other magazine strip in the same way to make a second handle. Then, glue both of the handles onto the top of the bag.

8. Cut four more strips of paper. Put a blob of glue in the middle of a strip and bend the ends onto it. Do the same with three more strips.

9. Glue the strips in the shape of a flower. Make a small paper loop and glue it onto the middle of the flower. Then, glue the flower onto the bag.

Printed flowers

You will need: paper and lots of things for printing, such as jar lids, nuts, pens, cardboard and pipecleaners or string.

You can use anything you find to print different shapes.

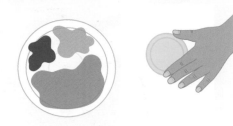

1. Spread different paints on an old plate. For the middle of a flower, dip a jar lid into some paint and press it onto the paper, near the top.

2. Dip a nut into some paint. Press it around the middle of the flower for petals. Then, dip the end of a pen into some paint and press it inside the nut shapes.

If you don't have a pipecleaner you could use string instead.

Press all along the pipe cleaner to print it.

3. Dip a strip of cardboard into some paint. Use one edge to print lines inside the flower. Add dots, too. Then, bend a pipe cleaner into the shape of a stem.

4. Dip the pipe cleaner into green paint and press it onto the paper. Then, bend another pipe cleaner into a leaf shape. Use it to print green leaves.

Print with all types of things to make a flower garden.

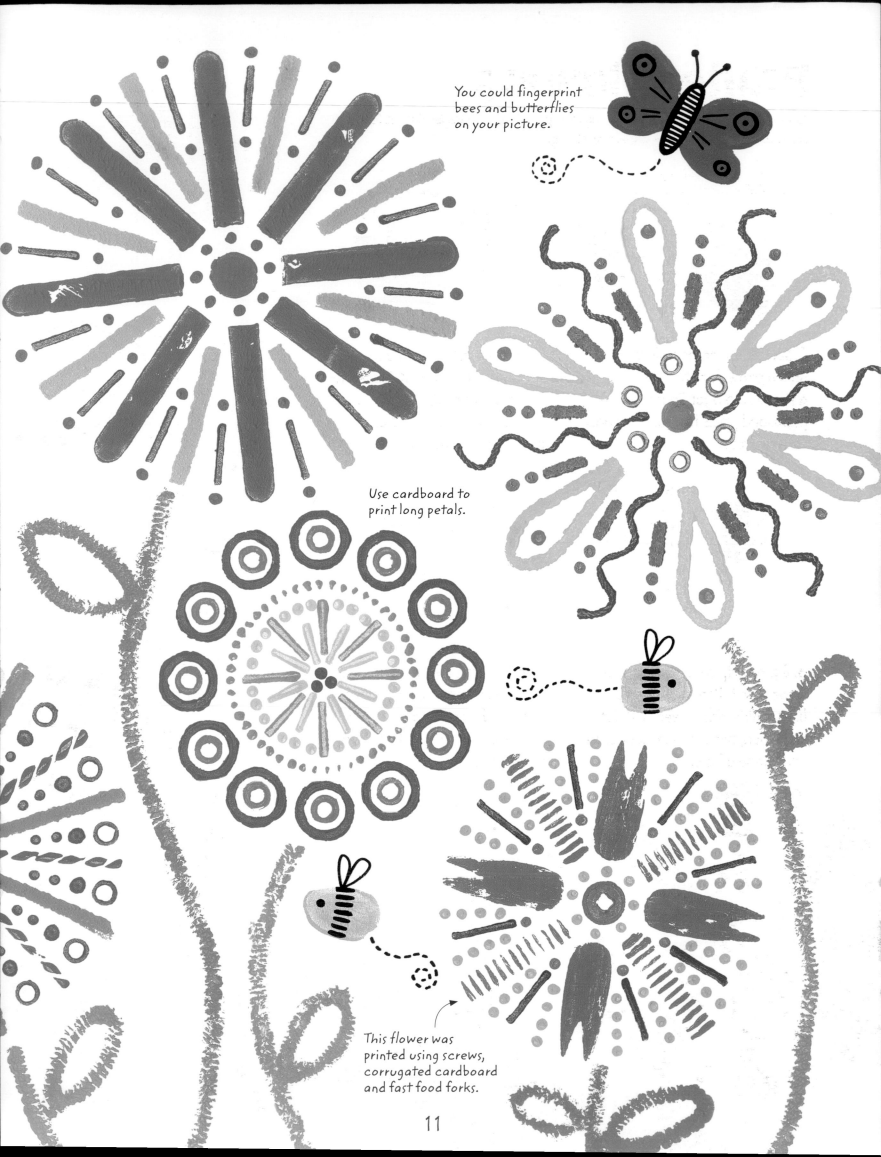

You could fingerprint bees and butterflies on your picture.

Use cardboard to print long petals.

This flower was printed using screws, corrugated cardboard and fast food forks.

11

Notebook covering

You will need: a notebook you want to cover, thin cardboard, wrapping paper and thick paper.

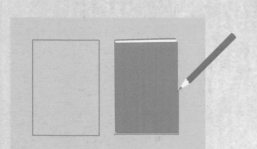

Leave a small space here so that the book can open.

You could use any paper such as wrapping paper or packing paper.

1. Lay a book you want to cover on a large piece of old thin cardboard. Draw around it. Then, draw around it again and cut out the shapes.

2. Glue one of the cardboard pieces onto the front cover of the book. Then, glue the other piece of cardboard onto the back of the book.

3. Open the book and lay the pages face down. Spread glue on the cardboard. Then, turn the book over again and press it onto some paper.

Don't paint the spine.

Back   Front

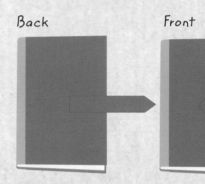

4. Cut around the book. Then, lay it face down on some old newspaper and draw two lines for the spine. Paint the back and front covers.

5. For a strap to secure your book, cut a long, thick strip from thick paper. Cut the corners off one end. Then, paint the strap and leave it to dry.

6. Glue the non-pointed end of the strap onto the back of the book. Then, bend the strap around the front of the book, like this.

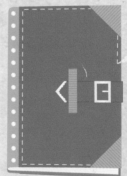

Draw lines for stitching, too.

7. Cut a thin strip, a little longer than the width of the strap. Then, spread glue on the ends of the strip and press it onto the the book over the strap.

8. Cut two squares from cardboard. Glue the squares onto the corners at the open edge of the book. Then, trim the edges of the cardboard.

9. Punch holes in paper with a hole puncher. Empty the puncher and glue the circles onto the book. Then, draw a buckle using a gold pen.

You could make a handbag book cover, taping on a piece of cord for a strap.

You could make a suitcase book cover. Find out how to make the handle on page 9.

This cover was decorated with old tickets and magazine pictures.

Dangly mobile

You will need: a box or jar lid and lots of bits and pieces, such as egg cartons, buttons and scraps of material.

Cut up straws and thread them onto the mobile.

You could add hearts cut from cardboard and scraps of material.

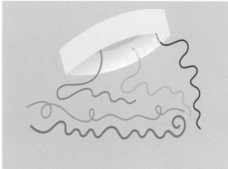

1. Lay a box lid on some old newspaper and paint it. When the paint is dry, tape pieces of yarn or old electrical wire around the inside of the lid.

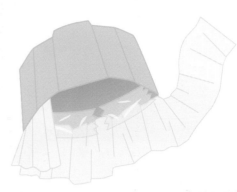

2. To make an egg carton 'flower', cut a cup off the carton. Cut a strip of tissue paper and glue it around the inside edge of the cup, like this.

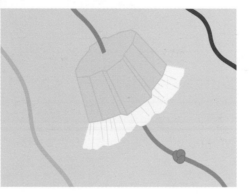

3. Push the tip of a ballpoint pen through the cup to make a hole. Then, thread it onto a piece of yarn on the mobile. Secure it with a knot.

4. You could cut flower shapes from pieces of old cardboard. Glue buttons onto the front of the flowers. Then, tape the flowers to the mobile.

5. Pinch together a small scrap of material. Then, wind one of the pieces of yarn around the material. Tie a knot in the yarn to secure the material.

6. You could thread some old beads onto the yarn. Tie a knot each time to keep them in place. Slide paperclips and small clips onto the mobile, too.

You can use any bits and pieces you find to hang on the mobile.

15

Gift tags

You will need: cardboard, scraps of material, paper and yarn, cord, string or ribbon.

1. Cut a rectangle with a curved end from cardboard. Then, spread glue on the cardboard. Press it onto some material and trim the edges.

2. Cut out hearts from two different papers and glue them onto the tag. Then, make a hole in the end of the tag using a hole puncher.

Loop

3. Fold a piece of ribbon or yarn in half and push it through the hole. Then, push the ends through the loop and pull them tight.

Use the ideas on this page to make lots of different gift tags.

Patterned boxes

You will need: old boxes with lids and magazines.

Cover the sides, too.

1. Cut magazine pages with different patterns on them into lots of small squares. Try to make all of the squares roughly the same size.

2. Spread white glue over the top of the the box lid. Then, starting at one edge of the lid, press the squares on until it is completely covered.

3. Cover the bottom of the box with squares in the same way. Let the glue dry, then trim any squares that overlap the edges of the box.

You could decorate a box with circles.

Find out how to make a gift tag on page 16.

Birds in a tree

You will need: corrugated cardboard, paper and scraps of material.

1. Lay a piece of corrugated cardboard with the slots going from top to bottom. Draw a teardrop shape for a bird's head and body, then cut it out.

Thin, slightly stiff material is ideal.

2. Draw an eye, and feathers on the neck. Cut a beak and a wing from scrap material and glue them on. Then, cut three tail feathers from more material.

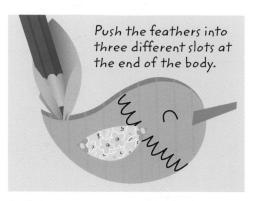

Push the feathers into three different slots at the end of the body.

3. Fold the end of a feather over the tip of a pencil. Push the pencil into a slot in the cardboard, then pull it out. The feather will stay in the slot.

4. Cut two thin strips from stiff cardboard for the bird's legs. Then, push each leg up into the slots at the bottom of the bird's body, like this.

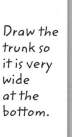

Draw the trunk so it is very wide at the bottom.

5. To make a tree, lay a piece of corrugated cardboard so the slots go from top to bottom. Then, draw a tree with six branches on the cardboard.

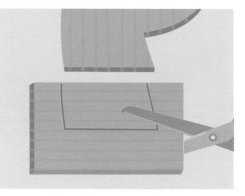

6. Cut out the tree. To make a base, lay the bottom of the trunk on another piece of cardboard and draw around it. Then, cut around the shape.

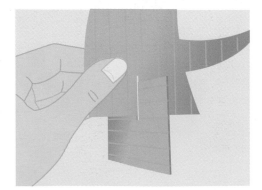

7. Cut a slit halfway down into the base. Then, cut a slit the same length up into the bottom of the trunk and slide the shapes together.

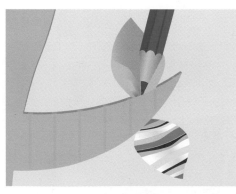

8. Cut some leaves from more pieces of scrap material. Use the tip of the pencil to push them into the slots at the ends of the branches.

9. To make a bird stand on the tree, slide its legs a little way into the slots in the cardboard part way along one of the branches.

You could use toothpicks for the birds' legs, instead of cardboard.

Make lots of different birds to stand on the branches of your tree.

To make an owl, draw its body with the slots going from side to side and push the wings into them.

Castle desk tidy

You will need: cardboard tubes and boxes, cardboard and scrap paper.

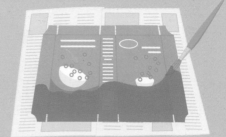

1. Follow the steps on page 32 to cut tubes and boxes to the right height for storing pens and pencils. Brush thick paint over them and let them dry.

You will use this to make battlements, a door and windows.

2. Brush bright paint over some cardboard (see page 32 to find out how to paint patterned cardboard). Then, leave the paint to dry.

Leave a space between each one.

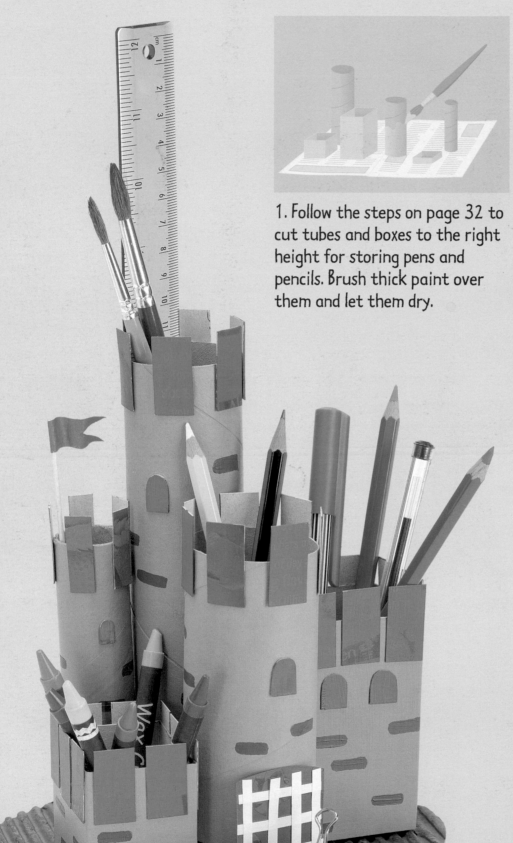

3. Cut lots of small rectangles from the painted cardboard for battlements. Then, glue them around the tops of the tubes and boxes.

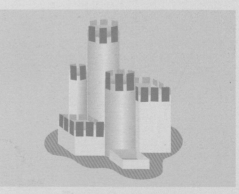

4. Cut a base from thick cardboard and paint it green. When the paint is dry, arrange the tubes and boxes on the base to look like a castle.

You could make a different kind of castle from any boxes and tubes you find.

This flag was cut from scrap paper and glued onto a toothpick, then taped inside the top of a tower.

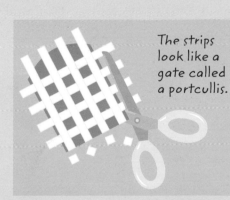

The strips look like a gate called a portcullis.

5. Brush white glue over the bottom of each tower, and where they touch each other. Glue the towers together, then press them onto the base.

6. Cut a door from the painted cardboard and some thin strips of paper. Glue the strips in a criss-cross pattern on the door and trim the ends.

7. Glue the door onto the castle. Cut arched windows from the painted cardboard and glue them on. Then, draw or paint a few bricks.

Truck collage

You will need: a piece of plain paper, food boxes and buttons.

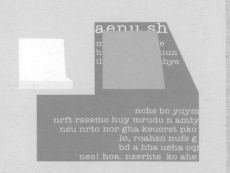

Glue the light just in front of the truck.

1. Cut a shape for a truck from a food box. Glue it onto a piece of plain paper. Then, cut shapes for a window and glue them onto the truck.

2. Cut out doors and glue them onto the truck. Then, cut a small rectangle for a door handle and a shape for a headlight. Glue them on.

3. To make a trailer, cut a square from thick paper. Then, cut thin strips from a bright food box. Glue them onto the trailer and trim the edges.

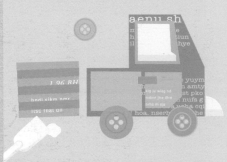

4. Glue the trailer onto the plain paper, a little way behind the truck. Then, dab glue below the truck and trailer, and press on buttons for wheels.

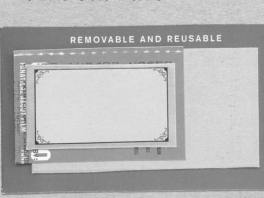

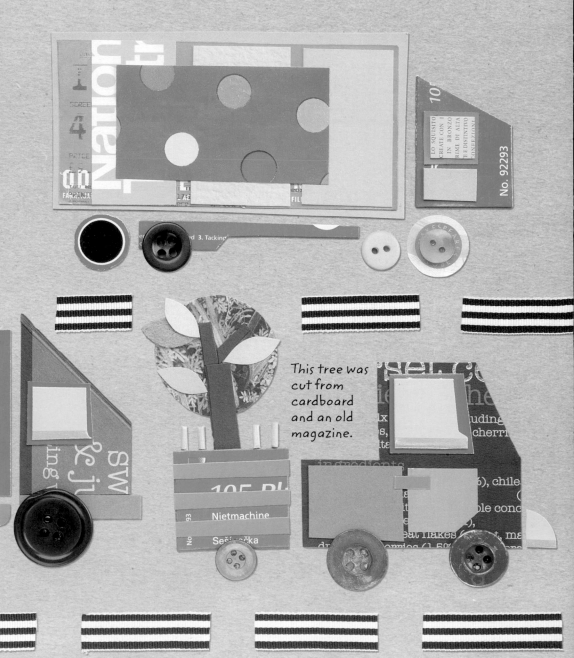

You could glue on pieces of ribbon for a road.

This tree was cut from cardboard and an old magazine.

Ribbon houses

You will need: paper, scraps of ribbon, cardboard and buttons.

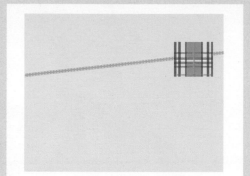

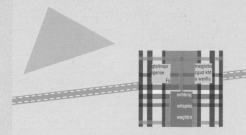

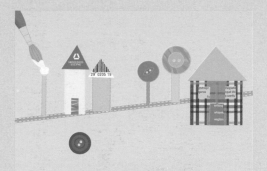

1. Cut a piece of thin ribbon for a road and glue it slanting across a piece of paper. Then, cut some thicker ribbon for a house and glue it on.

2. Cut a door and two windows from cardboard and glue them onto the house. Then, cut a triangular roof and glue it on top of the house.

3. For a tree, cut a short piece of ribbon for a trunk and glue it next to the house. Add a button for the tree top. Then, add more houses and trees.

You could add more roads, houses and trees to your picture.

Paper decorations

You will need: patterned wrapping paper, magazines or comics.

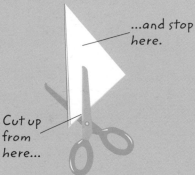

...and stop here.

Cut up from here...

1. Draw a 10cm x 10cm (4in x 4in) square on some paper and cut it out. Fold the square in half to make a triangle. Then, fold the triangle in half.

2. Make a cut into the shorter, open side of the triangle, about 2cm (1in) from the bottom. Stop cutting about 1cm (½in) from the folded side.

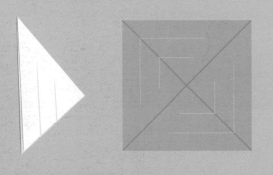

3. Make another cut into the triangle in the same way, a little way beside the first one, like this. Then, carefully unfold the paper.

4. Bend the inside flaps toward the middle of the square until they meet. Tape the flaps together. Then, turn over the decoration.

To make a star

5. Bend the next two flaps into the middle and tape them together in the same way, like this. Then, turn over the decoration again.

6. Bend the remaining flaps together and secure them with tape. Then, tape a thin piece of thread to the decoration to hang it up.

Make six of the paper decorations by following steps 1-6. Then, tape the ends of the decorations together in the shape of a star.

You could tape lots
of decorations to
one piece of string
or yarn and hang
them up.

Follow steps 8 and 9
on page 9 to make
a flower like this.

Plastic bag beads

You will need: a thin plastic bag and newspaper.

You don't need this piece.

The balls will be the beads, so roll lots if you want a long chain.

Tuck the plastic around the ball so you can't see the newspaper.

1. Smooth a thin plastic bag so that it is flat. Cut off the bottom of the bag. Then, cut a band from the bag that is a little wider than your hand.

2. Cut across the band to make a long strip, then tie a knot in one end of the strip. Rip small pieces of newspaper and roll each one into a ball.

3. Place one ball next to the knot in the strip. Pull the edges of the strip over the ball to cover it. Then, twist the plastic and tie a knot in it.

Trim off any excess plastic once you have knotted the ends.

4. Add more newspaper balls in the same way until you have finished the chain. Tie a knot after the last bead, then knot the ends together.

You could make a chain to go over your head for a necklace...

...or you could make a short chain for a bracelet.

Turn a head upside down to make an octopus.

Material heads

You will need: scraps of material, a magazine, cardboard and buttons.

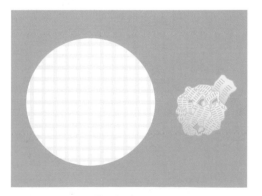

1. Lay a small plate on a piece of material and draw around it. Cut out the circle. Then, scrunch up a page from a magazine into a tight ball.

2. Put the paper ball in the middle of the material circle. Gather up the material around the ball and secure it with a rubber band.

3. Cut a mouth from cardboard and glue it onto the head. Glue on two buttons for eyes. Then, cut into the loose material for 'hair', like this.

Collage faces

You will need: cardboard, corrugated cardboard, newspaper, kitchen sponge and buttons.

The slots on the corrugated cardboard should be facing up.

1. Pour thick brown, white and black paint onto an old plate. Then, lay pieces of corrugated and smooth cardboard on some newspaper.

Only paint the ridges on the cardboard.

2. Dip a kitchen sponge into the brown paint. Then, rub it over piece of the corrugated cardboard. Do the same with some smooth cardboard.

This monster face was cut from a food box. Glue on fast food forks for teeth and bottle caps for a nose.

3. Paint another piece of smooth cardboard black in the same way. Then, paint some corrugated cardboard white. Leave the paint to dry.

Glue the ears behind the face.

4. Cut a face from another piece of cardboard. Then, cut a snout and ears from the brown corrugated cardboard. Glue them onto the face.

Glue the nose on top of the muzzle.

5. Cut two eyebrows from the smooth brown cardboard. Then, cut three white ovals for a muzzle, and a black nose. Glue the pieces onto the face.

This robot face was made by painting some shiny cardboard and using foil cases for eyelids.

You could make lots of faces and hang them up on a wall.

This will be the mane.

This is the back of the head.

6. Cut a page from an old newspaper in half. Fold over one of the shorter edges. Then, turn the paper over and fold the same edge over again.

7. Keep folding and turning until the paper is completely folded up. Then, fold two more half pages of newspaper in the same way.

8. Tape the newspaper onto the back of the lion's head, spreading the paper out as you tape it. Then, glue on two black buttons for eyes.

Dragon puppet

You will need: a cardboard tube, a narrow food box, large wrappers, corrugated cardboard, two satay or kebab sticks.

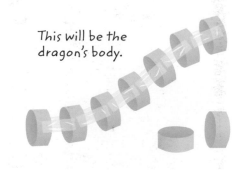

This will be the dragon's body.

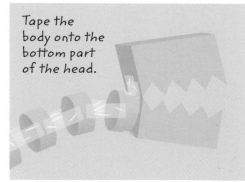

Tape the body onto the bottom part of the head.

1. Cut a cardboard tube into small, equal-sized pieces (see page 32). Leaving a gap between each one, join the pieces together using sticky tape.

2. Cut both ends from a box for the top and bottom of a dragon's head. Then, cut lots of triangles into the edges of the box ends for jagged teeth.

3. Slot the top of the head a little way inside the bottom and secure it with sticky tape. Then, tape the head to one end of the body, like this.

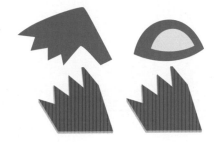

The slots in the corrugated cardboard must go from top to bottom.

4. Cut some large wrappers into long, thin strips. Then, starting at the head, glue the strips along the body, until it is completely covered.

5. To make a tail, cut more strips from wrappers and spread glue on half of each one. Then, press them around the end of the body, like this.

6. Cut out an ear and an eye from thin cardboard. Then, cut out two spines from corrugated cardboard. Paint all the shapes and the head. Let them dry.

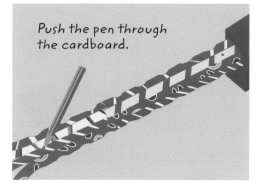

Push the pen through the cardboard.

If you don't have satay or kebab sticks, you could use pencils.

7. To make holes for the sticks, push the tip of a ballpoint pen through the top and bottom of the body, behind the head and at the end of the body.

8. Push a satay or kebab stick through each set of holes. Then, add the spines by sliding the ends of the sticks through the slots in the cardboard.

9. Glue the ear onto the head. Then, glue the eye on top of the ear. Use a black pen to draw an eyelid and pupil in the eye.

Move the sticks up and down to bend the dragon's body.

You could add fire coming out of the dragon's mouth using part of an orange plastic bag.

How to...

Strip a plastic wire

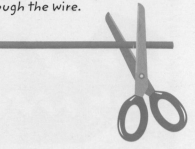

Don't cut all the way through the wire.

1. Using scissors, carefully cut a little way into the plastic covering near to the end of the wire. Then, turn the wire and cut again.

2. Keep turning and cutting until you have cut through the plastic all the way around. Then, carefully pull off the plastic, leaving the wire behind.

Follow the steps on this page to make legs from stripped wire.

Paint patterned cardboard

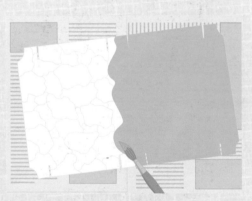

Lay the cardboard on some old newspaper. Paint the cardboard and let it dry. Then, if you can still see the pattern, paint the cardboard again.

If the cardboard has a very strong pattern, glue on lots of ripped-up pieces of tissue paper until it is covered. Then, paint the cardboard.

Cut a cardboard tube

Don't hold the tube too close to where you are cutting.

Lay the tube on a cutting board. Hold the tube still and gently saw into the top with a bread knife. Then, very carefully cut through the tube.

Cut a cardboard box

Snip into one edge of the cardboard box. Then, slide a scissor blade into the snip and cut around the box. Or, you can cut out the shape you need.

Photographic manipulation by John Russell.
First published in 2009 by Usborne Publishing Ltd., Usborne House, 83-85 Saffron Hill, London, England. www.usborne.com